truth

Danny Curtin

OUr JOUrNEY

At the beginning of our journey towards confirmation, we are going to think about our identity – what makes us the people we are? And about our dreams... what hopes do you have for the future? What sort of person do you want to be? What do you think God wants for you?

WE BEGIN WITH A PRAYER

Lord God,
As we begin this journey of faith together, we ask you to guide us along the way, and be patient with us as we follow. Support us, Lord, as we begin to ask questions, as we discuss issues and as we grow in our faith. We pray that you inspire us, Lord, to be open to your leadership in our lives.

Amen.

QUOTE

"Love is from God and everyone who loves is a child of God and knows God."

From the first letter of St John

What makes you happy?

What are the things in our lives that give us happiness? Do our friends make us happy? Does our family make us happy? How about our pets, school holidays, games consoles, the weather?

Think of something you have achieved, which you are pleased with.

What did you have to do to achieve this?

Think of something that happened that made you happy.

Why did it make you happy?

Think of something that happened which made you unhappy, or really wound you up.

Why did it make you unhappy?

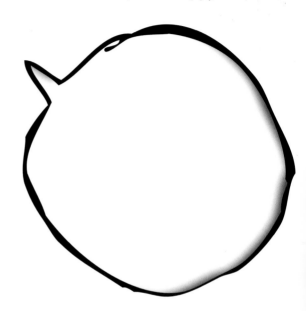

QUOTE

"The glory of God is a human being fully alive." *St Irenaeus*

DISCUSS

- Why did these issues make you happy/unhappy?
- What happened?
- Who was involved?
- Whom did it affect?
- How did they feel?

If you could write your own life story, where would you be in five years' time, ten years' time, and when you are 65 years old?

Five Years' Time:

Ten Years' Time:

When I'm 65 years old:

JUDGE

Glossary

"Parable"
A story Jesus told which had a deeper meaning.

A: Here is a **parable** Jesus told his disciples.
It is called "**The Lost Sheep**" (Luke chapter 15, verses 1-6).

"The tax collectors and the sinners were all seeking the company of Jesus to hear what he had to say, and the Pharisees and the scribes complained. 'This man,' they said, 'welcomes sinners and eats with them.'
So he spoke this parable to them:
'What man among you with a hundred sheep, losing one, would not leave the ninety-nine in the wilderness and go after the missing one till he found it? And when he found it, would he not joyfully take it on his shoulders and then, when he got home, call together his friends and neighbours?
'Rejoice with me,' he would say, 'I have found my sheep that was lost.'"

DiSCUSS

- Who is in this story?
- What happened?
- What was said?
- How might the people present have reacted? Why?
- What does this story say about how God views each one of us?
- What meaning does this story have for our lives?

B: What does our faith say?

Think about the people you love, and the people who love you.
Remember that YOU are very special to God. God loves you deeply.
He will **always** stay with you, even if you get lost along life's journey.

 **"I have come so that they may have life and have it to the full."** *From the Gospel of St John*

We are so special in God's eyes. We are told at the beginning of the Bible that we are made in "God's own image". This is the message of the story of the lost sheep too – we are worth so much to God that he will search us out and care for us.

Because God loves us, God want us all to be LOVING towards each other and to do GOOD to one another. When we're little, we're often told by adults to be "good". When they say this they're really asking us to behave ourselves and be nice. As we grow up we learn that being GOOD and being NICE can be two different things. What do you think the difference is? Talk about it with your friends.

This is how God wants us to be happy:

- To strive for **Goodness**
- To always **Love**.

What does this mean? Is this realistic?

C: God's life story for you

Look back at the answers you gave on page 7 about how you want your life to be in the future. How many of your answers agree with the values that you have discussed?

If you had to try and write your story, like God would write it, what do you think God would want for you, in five, ten years' time, or when you're 65? Use this space to write down your thoughts.

Five Years' Time:

Ten Years' Time:

When I'm 65 years old:

D: A sacramental sign

When you are confirmed you will be anointed with the oil of chrism. This oil is a sign of your life in God. Anointing, in biblical times, is rich in meaning: oil is a sign of abundance and joy, and marks someone as special – like kings and prophets, and guests to your house. It is a sweet smelling oil, and originally would have been very expensive. It is a sign that you are special in God's eyes, and worth more than money, or power, or anything else the world can provide.

Glossary

"Sacrament"
A sacrament is an outward sign that God is at work within us.

Anointing is God's way of communicating to us, that we are worth more than riches, and will have a fullness of life in God.

- In what ways are you shown that you are valued by other people?
- In what other ways do you know that you are valued by God?

ACE

Meet... Mwende

My name is Mwende. I came from Kenya two years ago. I'm still new to the country and I'm still learning new things. I enjoy being a Christian because it's something I like doing.

I serve in the church as an altar server, and it's something I do because I feel like I'm relaxed here. It's good for me because back home you don't have the opportunity to serve in the church, so being an altar server is a good honour for me.

I would like to be a nutritionist, and to help people know what's good for them and what's bad for them, and what they need to have in life to grow and prosper. An alternative to that: seeing young people happy makes me happy, so that encourages me to be a care worker, or someone who takes care of children.

José Antonio Abreu

A Professor of Economics who is also a government minister doesn't really sound like the kind of person to start a youth movement. But that is what José Antonio Abreu has done. He turned his Catholic faith into action. After a distinguished academic career and time spent as the culture minister for the government in his native Venezuela, José Antonio Abreu founded an organisation called El Sistema (The System). It brought classical music lessons to children in the slums. These children were often not in school and many were involved in crime. The capital city, Caracas, is one of the most violent places in the world. Many people thought his scheme would have no effect. They were wrong.

© Robyn Beck/AFP/Getty Images 2009.

Today more than 400,000 people are involved in El Sistema. Giving children in slums music lessons doesn't just give them the chance to play music, it widens their horizons, gives them a sense of achievement and teaches them skills. All around the world Venezuelan slum kids are getting jobs with top orchestras. One of these is Edicson Ruiz. When he was eleven he was given lessons on the double bass. He said having music in his life saved him: "When I woke up in the morning I didn't know if I would have any food to eat but I knew I could play music and feed my soul."

Today he plays with the Berlin Philharmonic Orchestra, one of the best orchestras in the world.

"Let us reveal to our children the beauty of music and music shall reveal to our children the beauty of life." *José Antonio Abreu*

Deciding on your action

So far we have looked at hopes and aspirations in life, and what causes sadness and happiness. We have thought about what our faith has to tell us about this. When we look at how our real lives and faith combine, it leads to action. Once we have thought through God's perspective on our lives, we are ready to decide on an action.

This week I am going to help bring God's goodness and love to:

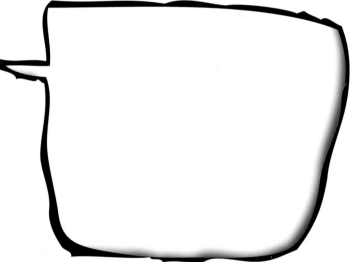

If you prefer, you can write this bit in when you get home, or keep it as a secret between you and God.

Next week we will hold each other to account for our actions, so if you want to you can share your experiences with the group then.

 **"This is my commandment: love one another, as I have loved you."** *From the Gospel of St John*

PRAYER

You don't need to be in church to pray. You can pray anywhere, anytime. Here are some prayers and Bible readings which can help you:

Psalm 139

Lord, you examine me and know me,
You know when I sit, when I rise,
You understand my thoughts from afar.
You watch when I walk or lie down,
You know every detail of my conduct.

A word is not yet on my tongue
Before you, Lord, know all about it.
You fence me in, behind and in front,
You have laid your hand upon me.
Such amazing knowledge is beyond me,
A height to which I cannot attain.

You created my inmost self,
Knit me together in my mother's womb.
For so many marvels I thank you;
A wonder am I, and all your works are wonders.

A prayer

Thank you, Lord,
for loving us into existence.
Thank you for helping us to understand
the world around us
and for inspiring us to change it for the better.
Protect us, Lord, as we follow you through this
    week.
Strengthen us in our quest for happiness for
    ourselves
and for all our friends.
Amen.

Our Father

Our Father who art in heaven,
hallowed be thy name.
Thy kingdom come.
Thy will be done
on earth as it is in heaven.
Give us this day our daily bread,
and forgive us our trespasses,
as we forgive those who trespass against us,
and lead us not into temptation,
but deliver us from evil.

A simple prayer

You, Lord, are goodness itself,
and the source of all goodness in the world.
Show me, Lord, how I can tap into that energy
and carry your goodness to the situations
that I am faced with in life.
Amen.

Why not try writing a prayer of your own in the space below? Use the prayer to talk to God about your identity – the person you are and the person you want to become. Talk to God about being a **GOOD** and **LOVING** person.

More Bible readings about love...

Matthew 22: 37-39

Jesus said to him "You must love the Lord your God with all your heart, with all your soul, and with all your mind. This is the greatest and the first commandment. The second resembles it: You must love your neighbour as yourself."

1 John 4:16

We have recognised for ourselves, and put our faith in, the love God has for us.
God is love, and whoever remains in love remains in God and God in him.

1 Corinthians 13:4-13

Love is always patient and kind; love is never jealous; love is not boastful or conceited, it is never rude and never seeks its own advantage, it does not take offence or store up grievances. Love does not rejoice at wrongdoing, but finds its joy in the truth. It is always ready to make allowances, to trust, to hope and to endure whatever comes.

Love never comes to an end. But if there are prophecies, they will be done away with; if tongues, they will fall silent; and if knowledge, it will be done away with. For we know only imperfectly, and we prophesy imperfectly; but once perfection comes, all imperfect things will be done away with.

When I was a child, I used to talk like a child, and see things as a child does, and think like a child; but now that I have become an adult, I have finished with all childish ways. Now we see only reflections in a mirror, mere riddles, but then we shall be seeing face to face. Now I can know only imperfectly; but then I shall know just as fully as I am myself known.

As it is, these remain: faith, hope and love, the three of them; and the greatest of them is love.

BapLism - winning The LotteRy

SESSION 2

When we were baptised we were welcomed into God's family – the Church. Most people are baptised as babies and at a child's baptism the parents and godparents make promises on behalf of the child. Confirmation is our chance to make those promises to God ourselves.

WE BEGIN WITH A PRAYER

Loving Lord Jesus,
When you were baptised you showed the world that you were one with God our Father. Thank you for giving us the gift of baptism, making each one of us a part of your family in the Church. Through our session today may we come to a greater understanding of you so that we may grow as Christians in your love.

Amen.

QUOTE

"You must see what great love the Father has lavished on us by letting us be called God's children – which is what we are!"

From the first letter of St John

What does being a Christian mean to you?

Write down three things that you do because you are a Christian.

Write down three things that make it hard to be a Christian.

Belonging to a group

What groups do you belong to? Are you sporty? Or in a music group? Are you involved in your local community or do you have a hobby that you share with other people who are interested in the same things? What about groups you belong to that aren't so formal? What groups define you as a person? Is it the music you listen to? The kinds of clothes you like to wear? Your hairstyle? The people you try to be like? Write down a few things that define you.

What groups do you belong to?

What do these groups expect from you?

What do you expect from them?

As Christians we have special ways of marking out our belonging to the Church. First there was our baptism, this was when we joined the group, it is the first of the sacraments of Christian initiation. Now we are preparing for the sacrament of confirmation. This is a time to stand up and be confirmed in the faith we were given as children.

JUDGE

A: This is a reading from St Matthew's **Gospel** about when Jesus was baptised.
It is called "**The Baptism of the Lord**"
Matthew chapter 3, verses 13-17

"Jesus came from Galilee to the Jordan to be baptised by John. John tried to dissuade him, with the words, 'It is I who need baptism from you, and yet you come to me!' But Jesus replied, 'Leave it like this for the time being; it is fitting that we should, in this way, do all that uprightness demands.' Then John gave in to him.

And when Jesus had been baptised he at once came up from the water, and suddenly the heavens opened and he saw the Spirit of God descending like a dove and coming down on him. And suddenly there was a voice from heaven, 'This is my Son, the Beloved; my favour rests on him.'"

 **DISCUSS**

- Who is in this story?
- What happened?
- What was said?
- How might the people present have reacted? Why?
- What does this story say about our baptism?

When Jesus was baptised two very important things happened.

1. The Holy Spirit descended upon Jesus.
2. God the Father revealed Jesus as his "beloved Son".

At our Baptism we were declared a child of God and given the gift of the Spirit.

It may help to imagine winning the lottery! When we win the lottery we've won the moment our numbers come up, but we still need to go and claim our prize money. When we were conceived and God gave us life, we won the lottery. We are made a child of God. Our baptism is the moment we claim the prize. We claim the fact that we are children of God and receive our prize – the gift of the Holy Spirit to help us to live like true lottery winners!

What do you think of this idea?

Can you think of any ways in which being part of the Church isn't like winning the Lottery?

 **"Peter answered… 'every one of you must be baptised in the name of Jesus Christ for the forgiveness of your sins, and you will receive the gift of the Holy Spirit.'"** *From the Acts of the Apostles*

B: What does our faith say?

"What marks us in the eyes of our enemies is our loving kindness. 'Only look,' they say, 'look how they love one another.' "

An ancient Christian philosopher called Tertullian wrote this down in the second century AD to explain what Roman citizens made of Christians at the time.

At baptism we are "reborn" as children of God. We belong to God's family. Baptism is our initiation ceremony into the family of God.

When we receive the gift of the Holy Spirit, it involves an obligation to respond to that gift. From the moment we are baptised we are meant to live our lives for God, continuing the work of Jesus in the world. As Christians, we should live differently and people should know who we are.

What marks you out as a Christian?

How can people around us know that we are Christian?

What does being Christian mean in our daily lives?

"Jesus said, 'John baptised with water but, not many days from now, you are going to be baptised with the Holy Spirit.'"

From the Acts of the Apostles

C: A Sacramental Sign

When you were baptised there were two main signs: *water* and *oil*.

What does the water symbolise?

What does the oil symbolise?

Why do you think these two symbols are used in baptism?

We are preparing for the sacrament of confirmation when we repeat for ourselves the promises made on our behalf when we were baptised. The gifts we receive at confirmation will help us to fulfil these promises.

These are the promises which were spoken by your parents and godparents at your baptism. The texts of the promises are given here. Read them through and think about whether you agree to them all.

Glossary

"Baptism"
The word baptism comes from the Greek word for immersion. In baptism our sins are washed away and we are reborn as God's children.

Priest: Dear parents and godparents:
You have come here to present this child for **baptism**. By water and the Holy Spirit he/she is to receive the gift of new life from God, who is love. On your part, you must make it your constant care to bring him/her up in the practice of the faith. See that the divine life which God gives him/her is kept safe from the poison of sin, to grow always stronger in his/her heart.
If your faith makes you ready to accept this responsibility, renew now the vows of your own baptism. Reject sin; profess your faith in Christ Jesus. This is the faith of the Church. This is the faith in which this child is about to be baptised.

Do you renounce Satan?
Parents & Godparents: **I do.**

Priest: And all his works?
Parents & Godparents: **I do.**

Priest: And all his empty show?
Parents & Godparents: **I do.**

Priest: Do you believe in God, the Father almighty, Creator of heaven and earth?
Parents & Godparents: **I do.**

Priest: Do you believe in Jesus Christ, his only Son, our Lord, who was born of the Virgin Mary, suffered death and was buried, rose again from the dead and is seated at the right hand of the Father?
Parents & Godparents: **I do.**

Priest: Do you believe in the Holy Spirit, the holy Catholic Church, the communion of saints, the forgiveness of sins, the resurrection of the body, and life everlasting?
Parents & Godparents: **I do.**

Priest: This is our faith. This is the faith of the Church. We are proud to profess it, in Christ Jesus our Lord.
All: **Amen.**

QUOTE

"It is better to be the child of God than king of the whole world." *St Aloysius Gonzaga*

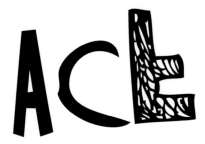

Meet... Michael

My Catholic faith has a place in every aspect of my life. And so, even if I don't take everything to heart every single second of my life, it does create certain guidelines and certain values that I've taken as my own, which help me to make better decisions.

Overall, I think faith is something personal, that you look to find comfort and guidance from. There are 1.2 billion Catholics worldwide, 1.2 billion different interpretations of the faith. But it's just one faith, and there are core things that draw us in together to be Catholic: we believe in God, we believe in the life of Jesus.

But I think there are lots of rules that we have to question so that our faith can sit right with us. And it's only through questioning things that we get to the truth.

Frank Cottrell Boyce

I'm a Catholic and I write movies. Faith and cinema have always been connected in my mind, partly because when I was little I used sometimes to go to a church in a converted cinema – it still had velvety flip seats, instead of pews and a big screen behind the altar.

My first job was writing soap opera (*Coronation Street*). I loved it but in the end I knew other people could write it just as well – or better – than I could. Whatever you do creatively, in the end, you have to find the thing that only you can do, the thing that uses all of you.

So I started to write my faith in a lot more. I wrote a film called *Millions* – which is about a little boy whose Mum has died and who sees saints. A lot of people thought that seeing saints was a sign of mental disturbance, whereas I thought it was a blessing. Fortunately I had a great director, Danny Boyle, on my side and he stood up for me. I was worried that sticking so strongly to a Catholic point of view would alienate people, but it's had the opposite effect.

As a Catholic I have a common bond with millions of other Catholics all over the world. Cinema is just the same. It tries to find stories that work for everyone, all over the world. It tries to strike that common chord. A lot of people find that really hard to do but as a Catholic it's just part of how I think. We are all sons and daughters of God, and all brothers and sisters in the Spirit of Christ – a great family.

Frank Cottrell Boyce is a patron of Missio, which helps to share faith and connect people and churches throughout the world. For more information see www.missio.org.uk

"I think people can sense that you're putting all of yourself into something and they respect that."
Frank Cottrell Boyce

© Macmillan Children's Books

Deciding on your action

So far we have looked at how we have been made part of the Church community through our baptism and at how we all belong to different groups. We have also thought about what happened at baptism both for Jesus at his baptism and for us when we were baptised.

When we look at how our real lives and faith combine, it leads to action. Once we have thought through God's perspective on our lives we are ready to decide on an action.

Think about what you promised to do last week. Did you do it? How did it go? How did you feel? If you want to share your experience with the group you can but you are under no pressure to share this if you don't want to.

Think about what you might do this week:

This week I am going to help

to recognise that they are loved and valued by doing:

If you prefer, you can write this bit in when you get home, or keep it as a secret between you and God.

Choosing a confirmation name

At your confirmation you will be given a new name, which you will have chosen for yourself. It needs to be a name which is shared by a saint.

Write names you are thinking of in this space, find out some more about the saints and then choose yourself a new name!

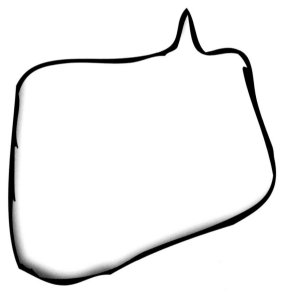

Choosing a sponsor

You also need to choose a sponsor.
This will be an adult confirmed Catholic who will stand beside you at the moment you receive the Holy Spirit in confirmation and who will be willing to act as a Christian guide throughout life. Think about who you could ask and write the name/s down in this space. Start asking the person you want soon so that you can make sure they are available on your confirmation day.

PRAYER

You don't need to be in church to pray. You can pray anywhere, anytime. Here are some prayers and Bible readings which can help you:

A prayer

Loving God,
we bring before you our concerns and our hopes.
We thank you for making us your children.
May we travel towards the sacrament of confirmation
confident in your love,
knowing that you will grant us the strength to follow you
even when it is difficult to stay faithful to your ways.
Amen.

From St Paul's letter to the Romans

This is a reading from a letter which St Paul wrote to the Christian community living in Rome. They were being persecuted by the Romans for their faith and Paul wrote to encourage them to stay faithful to Jesus:

"All who are guided by the Spirit of God are children of God; for what you received was not the spirit of slavery to bring you back into fear; you received the Spirit of adoption, enabling us to cry out 'Abba, Father!' The Spirit himself joins with our spirit to bear witness that we are children of God. And if we are children, then we are heirs, heirs of God and joint-heirs with Christ."

A simple prayer

Thank you, Lord,
for welcoming us into your family, the Church.
Through your love for us we will grow and
become the people you intend us to be.
May we come closer to you as we go
through this week
and for the rest of our lives.
Amen.

The prayer of St Richard of Chichester

Thanks be to you, our Lord Jesus Christ,
for all the benefits which you have given us,
for all the pains and insults which you have
borne for us.
Most merciful Redeemer, Friend and Brother,
may we know you more clearly,
love you more dearly,
and follow you more nearly,
day by day.
Amen.

Why not try writing a prayer of your own in
the space below? Use the prayer to talk to
God about your identity – the person you
are and the person you want to become.
Talk to God about being a member of God's
family and what that means to you.

More Bible readings about being baptised and being part of God's family...

Mark 10:14

Jesus said, "Let the little children come to me; do not stop them; for it is to such as these that the kingdom of God belongs."

Acts 2:38-41

"You must repent," Peter answered, "and every one of you must be baptised in the name of Jesus Christ for the forgiveness of your sins, and you will receive the gift of the Holy Spirit. The promise that was made is for you and your children, and for all those who are far away, for all those whom the Lord our God is calling to himself." ...They accepted what he said and were baptised. That very day about three thousand were added to their number.

From Psalm 89

I will sing for ever of your love, O Lord;
Through all ages my mouth will proclaim your truth.
Of this I am sure, that your love lasts for ever,
That your truth is firmly established as the heavens.

The heavens are yours, the world is yours.
It is you who founded the earth and all it holds;
It is you who created the North and the South,
Tabor and Hermon shout with joy at your name.

Yours is a mighty arm, O Lord;
Your hand is strong, your right hand ready.
Justice and right are the pillars of your throne,
Love and truth walk in your presence.

Happy the people who acclaim such a king,
Who walk, O Lord, in the light of your face,
Who find their joy every day in your name,
Who make your justice the source of their bliss.

CONFIRMATION – CONFIRMING OUR ROLE

SESSION 3

Nobody likes having to ask for help and yet we all need help sometimes. As Christians we know that God is always there to help us through difficult times. Today we are going to think about what is going to happen at your confirmation. At confirmation you will receive the gifts of the Holy Spirit and with that, the promise of God's help for your whole life.

WE BEGIN WITH A PRAYER

Dear Lord,
We gather again today to hear your word and to learn more about you.
Thank you for your presence among us here, now and always.
As we prepare for our confirmation we ask that we may be guided by your Holy Spirit
so that we may listen, understand and grow in the light of your love.

Amen.

QUOTE

"Now Christ's body is yourselves, each of you with a part to play in the whole."

From the first letter St Paul sent to the Corinthians

If I were a…

If I were a fictional character I would be...

because...

If I were an animal I would be a...

because...

If I were a kind of food I would be a...

because...

What does this say about you?
Can you think of any other things you could imagine yourself as? What would they say about you?

Why are you going to be confirmed?

What is the main reason you are going to be confirmed? *(Be honest!)*

Has anyone influenced your decision?

Help!

Name something that you have needed help with recently.
It doesn't matter how large or small this is.

Name one way in which you have responded to someone else's
needs recently.

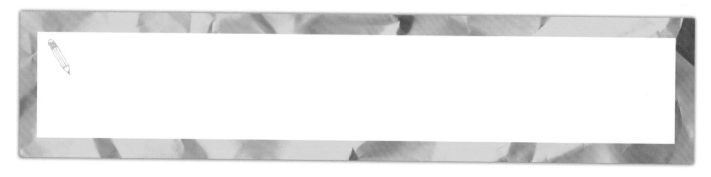

Can you think of any areas where you currently need help, or can you think of someone you know who needs some support?

What do you think the word "faith" means?

Is your Catholic faith important to you?

JUDGE

A: This is the story about what happened when the Holy Spirit came upon the apostles.

This reading comes from the second chapter of the book of the **Acts of the Apostles**.

"When Pentecost day came round, they had all met together, when suddenly there came from heaven a sound as of a violent wind which filled the entire house in which they were sitting; and there appeared to them tongues as of fire; these separated and came to rest on the head of each of them. They were all filled with the Holy Spirit and began to speak different languages as the Spirit gave them power to express themselves."

DISCUSS

- Who is in this story?(And who is missing from this story?)
- What happened?
- What was said?
- How might the people present have reacted? Why?
- How do you think you might have reacted if you had been there?
- What does this story tell us about what Jesus has done to support his followers?

B: What does our faith say?

When you are confirmed you will receive the seven gifts of the Holy Spirit.

What do you think they mean?

1. Wisdom
   means:

2. Understanding
   means:

3. Right Judgement *(also sometimes called "counsel")*
   means:

4. Courage *(also sometimes called "fortitude")*
   means:

5. **Knowledge**
means:

6. **Reverence** *(also sometimes called "piety")*
means:

7. **Awe of God**
(also sometimes called "fear of God")
means:

Think about...
...when you could put these gifts into practice. Think about your school, your parish, your family and your friends.

"Send forth your Spirit, O Lord, and renew the face of the earth." *From Psalm 104*

C: A sacramental sign

Our faith tells us that at confirmation our baptism is confirmed and that we are sealed with the gift of the Holy Spirit.

> **There are two main signs used at confirmation:**
> - The laying on of hands
> - And the anointing with the oil of **chrism**.

> **Why do you think these two signs are used at confirmation?**

What do they tell us about what happens at confirmation?

"Open your hearts to the love God instils... God loves you tenderly. What He gives you is not to be kept under lock and key, but to be shared." *St Teresa of Calcutta*

ACE

Meet... John Jo

I'm John Jo and I'm fifteen. What I think it means to be a Catholic is showing your love and appreciation for what God has given you in everyday life.

I took up charity work with the national society for epilepsy because my sister was diagnosed with epilepsy a few years ago. And I've had to deal with the traumatic times when she's had a fit and I've been on my own. I've had to grow up in that situation and learn some of the horrible truths of life. I think it shouldn't have to be that horrible for someone else of my age. And I think I could make that happen with charity work.

In my school I organized an own clothes day single handedly and we raised £2,000 for this, and the charity were very grateful.

Frank Skinner

Frank Skinner is an award-winning comedian, television and radio host, author and podcaster. He was born Christopher Graham Collins in West Bromwich in 1957. He left school with no qualifications and worked in a metal factory. He enrolled in night school and eventually enrolled at University and graduated with a Masters degree in English literature.

Frank's live career began in 1987 when he spent £400 of his last £435 booking a room at the Edinburgh Festival Fringe. Four years later in 1991 he returned to the city and took home comedy's most prestigious prize, The Perrier Award.

At the 2001 British Comedy Awards, he was named Best Comedy Entertainment Personality. Since 2009 he has hosted The Frank Skinner Show on Absolute Radio, broadcast live on Saturdays and later released as a podcast.

Along with David Baddiel, he provided vocals and wrote the lyrics for "Three Lions", the official song in collaboration with Liverpudlian indie band The Lightning Seeds, to mark the England national football team's participation in the 1996 European Championship (which was hosted in England).

QUOTE

"Not only has it [the Church] brought me a sense of where I am in the world and how I should be with other people, it has also encouraged my imagination to think widely. And when I'm in a Catholic church wherever I am in the world, I feel at home." - *From an interview with The Guardian, January 2014*

Deciding on your action

So far we have looked at the times when we have needed help and times when we have received help. We have learned about the gifts of the Holy Spirit and about the help that these offer us in our our lives.

When we look at how our real lives and faith combine, it leads to action. Once we have thought through God's perspective on our lives we are ready to decide on an action.

Think about what you promised to do last week. Did you do it? How did it go? How did you feel? If you want to share your experience with the group you can but you are under no pressure to share this if you don't want to.

Think about how the gifts of Holy Spirit can be used in your life (whether at home or school, in your church or with friends). Now decide what you will do this week.

This week I am going to help

to

If you prefer, you can write this bit in when you get home, or keep it as a secret between you and God.

PRAYER

You don't need to be in church to pray. You can pray anywhere, anytime. Here are some prayers and Bible readings which can help you:

Psalm 121
I lift up my eyes to the mountains;
Where is my help to come from?
My help comes from the Lord
Who made heaven and earth.

May he save your foot from stumbling;
May he, your guardian, not fall asleep!
You see – he neither sleeps nor slumbers,
The guardian of Israel.

The Lord is your guardian, your shade,
The Lord at your right hand.
By day the sun will not strike you,
Nor the moon by night.

The Lord guards you from all harm
The Lord guards your life.
The Lord guards your comings and goings,
Henceforth and for ever.

A prayer
We thank you, Lord, for giving us life.
We thank you for sending your Holy Spirit to
live within our hearts.
We thank you for creating us with a purpose.
May we go out this week full of your love
so that we may share your saving help with
others in the ways that we listen, in the ways
that we speak and in the acts that we do.
Amen.

A prayer of St Edmund of Abingdon

Lord, since you exist, we exist. Since you are beautiful, we are beautiful. Since you are good, we are good. By our existence we honour you. By our beauty we glorify you. By our goodness we love you.

Lord, through your power all things were made. Through your wisdom all things are governed. Through your grace all things are sustained. Give us power to serve you, wisdom to discern your laws and grace to obey those at all times. Amen.

Why not try writing a prayer of your own in the space on the right? Use the prayer to talk to God about your identity – the person you are and the person you want to become. Perhaps you could talk to God about something you need help with.

A simple prayer

Dear Jesus,
By the power of your Holy Spirit I can achieve what you want for me in my life.
May I remember to call on your help when I need it
So that I can live fully in your love.
Amen.

More Bible readings about God's help...

John 14:15-18
If you love me, you will keep my commandments. I shall ask the Father and he will give you another comforter to be with you for ever, the Spirit of truth whom the world can never accept since it neither sees nor knows him; but you know him, because he is with you, he is in you. I shall not leave you orphans; I shall come to you.

Exodus 15:2
The Lord is my strength and my song,
to him I owe my deliverance.
He is my God and I shall praise him,
My father's God and I shall extol him.

Romans 15:1-2
It is for us who are strong to bear with the susceptibilities of the weaker ones, and not please ourselves. Each of us must consider his neighbour's good, so that we support one another.

GETTiNG iT RiGHT WiTH GOD'S HELP

SESSiON 4

We don't know what the future holds for any of us. But we do know that we have some choice in the matter. Every day we are faced with decisions to make. From deciding what to wear in the morning to deciding whether to get married, life forces us to make choices. Sometimes we make good choices, sometimes we choose the wrong thing. As Christians we can access the best advice line possible every time we need to make a decision – we have a direct line to God.

WE BEGIN WITH A PRAYER

Dear Lord,
We ask that you bless our time here together today. We ask that you will fill our hearts with your love and inspire us to listen to your words. We open our hearts to receive your goodness and love.

Amen.

QUOTE

"The Lord is my shepherd… he guides me along the right path."
From Psalm 23

What are you going to do with your life?

What is one decision you have made which you are proud of?

Can you think of a decision you made which went horribly wrong?

Think about your life and the how you choose to live it. Our choices, or decisions, are one of the most determining factors in our lives. Usually we make decisions based on our principles.

What do you understand a principle to be?

Name three principles you hope to live by as you grow as a young adult in the world.

1.

2.

3.

What do you think the Christian moral code is?

"It is not so essential to think much as to love much." *St Teresa of Jesus*

JUDGE

Glossary

"Commandments"
In the Old Testament, God gave Moses the Ten Commandments.

A: This is one of the most important bits of teaching which Jesus gave.

This reading comes from the twelfth chapter of St Mark's Gospel.

"One of the scribes who had listened to them debating appreciated that Jesus had given a good answer and put a further question to him "which is the first of all the **commandments**?" Jesus replied, "This is the first: *Listen, Israel, the Lord our God is the one, only Lord and you must love the Lord your God with all your heart, with all your soul, with all your mind and with all your strength*." The second is this: *You must love your neighbour as yourself*. There is no commandment greater than these."

DiSCUSS

- Who is in this story?
- What happened?
- What was said?
- How might the people present have reacted? Why?
- What does this story tell us about what is important in our own lives?

What do you think St Augustine meant by this?

"**Love God and then do what you want!**" *St Augustine*

B: The beatitudes (or the "Be Attitudes")
This reading comes from St Matthew's Gospel.

"How blessed are the poor in spirit: the kingdom of heaven is theirs.
Blessed are the gentle: they shall have the earth as their inheritance.
Blessed are those who mourn: they shall be comforted.
Blessed are those who hunger and thirst for uprightness: they shall have their fill.
Blessed are the merciful: they shall have mercy shown them.
Blessed are the pure in heart: they shall see God.
Blessed are the peacemakers: they shall be recognised as children of God.
Blessed are those who are persecuted in the cause of uprightness: the kingdom of heaven is theirs.
Blessed are you when people abuse you and persecute you and speak all kinds of calumny against you falsely on my account. Rejoice and be glad, for your reward will be great in heaven."

Does this reading offer a guide for how to be?

What would a list of characteristics from this reading look like?

Do you think these are good principles to live by today? Why?

C: What does our faith say?

Jesus passed on his authority to his twelve apostles, before he ascended into heaven. Those twelve men continued to pass on their authority through ordaining others, whom we now call bishops. These bishops work together to continue to give us guidance as to how we should try to live. There are often things in our lives which Jesus never talked about, such as nuclear warfare, abortion, genetic engineering or the rights and wrongs of modern economic policies. For these things and a whole host of others, the Church provides teaching we can refer to in order to guide us.

Do you agree that we should listen to what the Church teaches?

We also believe that Jesus gave the Church seven sacraments, through which God continues to communicate with us and to offer us help. In the sacraments Jesus is present, showing us the love and support of God. God uses all our senses to communicate with us through the sacraments. We see, touch, hear, smell and even taste!

The seven sacraments are:

"Who except God can give you peace? Has the world ever been able to satisfy the heart?" *St Gerard Majella*

ACE

Meet... Katherine

Hello, my name's Katherine, and I'm 15. My faith has a massive impact on my life.

When I go through tough personal experiences I always pray to God, and it helps me get through it, helps kind of relax me. It's like I'm having a personal conversation with a friend, someone I've known for ever.

My dad was in hospital about three years ago, and I found it quite hard to talk to anyone about it. So I turned to God and prayed to him, and I knew that other people were praying as well. And I felt that if other people were praying to God then it would be okay.

If I didn't have my faith, I'd be worried because I'd be thinking that nothing could improve. I think if I'm praying to someone, then life is going to get better.

Pelé

Ask any football fan to name some of the greatest footballers ever and one name is bound to come high up their list. Pelé. In his home nation, Brazil, he is nicknamed "O Rei do Futebol" – " the King of Football". He is the only footballer to have lifted the World Cup three times and has scored more goals for Brazil than any other player before or since. His heyday was the 1960s and 1970s but since his retirement from playing in 1977 he has used his fame and influence in both international football and to work for children living in poverty.

Pelé's real name is Edison Arantes do Nascimento. He was born to a poor family in a *favela* – a shanty town – in Sao Paolo in 1940. As a child he didn't own a football and played with a sock stuffed with newspaper. His dad, who had tried to be a professional footballer before injury ruined his career, taught Pelé how to play. Since he was talent spotted as a teenager Pelé has become one of the most famous footballers of all time and one of the greatest Catholic sportspeople the world has seen.

© Christopher Furlong/Getty Images 2007

QUOTE

"God gave me the gift of knowing how to play soccer – because it really is a gift from God – and my father taught me to use it, he taught me the importance of always being ready and prepared, and that in addition to being a good player I should also be a good man." *Pelé*

Deciding on your action

So far today we have thought about making decisions and about how we are called to love one another. We have also thought about how the Holy Spirit is always present to help and guide us. When we look at how our real lives and faith combine, it leads to action. Once we have thought through God's perspective on our lives we are ready to decide on an action. What are you going to do this week?

Think about the beatitudes a few pages ago. Do they inspire you to choose to do something different this week?

This week I am going to:

If you prefer, you can write this bit in when you get home, or keep it as a secret between you and God.

"The Christian does not think God will love us because we are good, but that God will make us good because God loves us." *C.S. Lewis*

PRAYER

You don't need to be in church to pray. You can pray anywhere, anytime. Here are some prayers and Bible readings which can help you:

A prayer of St Thérèse of Lisieux, a French nun who died in 1897 aged just 24.

May today there be peace within.
May you trust God that you are exactly where you are meant to be.
May you not forget the infinite possibilities that are born of faith.
May you use those gifts that you have received, and pass on the love that has been given to you.
May you be content knowing you are a child of God.
Let this presence settle into your bones, and allow your soul the freedom to sing, dance, praise and love.
It is there for each and every one of us.
Amen.

A prayer

Lord, we gather here and bring our prayer intentions before you. We know that you will listen to our wants and needs and we know that you will respond with love towards us. Fill our hearts with your love and inspire us to be the best we can be by modelling ourselves on your example.
Amen.

A simple prayer

Loving Lord Jesus,
As we go through life, we are constantly faced with decisions to make. We know that you have asked us to love one another. May that command influence all our decisions so that we may act with love and follow your ways.
Amen.

Psalm 23

The Lord is my shepherd;
There is nothing I shall want.
Fresh and green are the pastures
Where he gives me repose.
Near restful waters he leads me,
To revive my drooping spirit.

He guides me along the right path;
He is true to his name.
If I should walk in the valley of darkness
No evil would I fear.
You are there with your crook and your staff;
With these you give me comfort.

You have prepared a banquet for me
In the sight of my foes.
My head you have anointed with oil;
My cup is overflowing.

Surely goodness and kindness shall follow me
All the days of my life.
In the Lord's own house shall I dwell
For ever and ever.

Why not try writing a prayer of your own in the space below? Use the prayer to talk to God about your identity – the person you are and the person you want to become. Perhaps you could talk to God about something you need help with.

More Bible readings about God's help...

Psalm 25
Lord, make me know your ways.
Lord, teach me your paths.
Make me walk in your truth, and teach me:
For you are God my saviour.

Luke 1: 46
This is the prayer Mary spoke to her cousin Elizabeth when they were both pregnant. Mary was pregnant with Jesus and Elizabeth was pregnant with John the Baptist.

My soul proclaims the greatness of the Lord
And my spirit rejoices in God my saviour;
Because he has looked upon his lowly handmaid.
Yes, from now onwards all generations will call me blessed,
For the Almighty has done great things for me.
Holy is his name,
And his faithful love extends age after age to those who fear him.
He has used the power of his arm, he has routed the arrogant of heart.
He has pulled down princes from their thrones and raised high the lowly.
He has filled the starving with good things, sent the rich away empty.

Romans 8
This comes from a letter which St Paul wrote to Christians who were being persecuted in Rome

If God is for us, who can be against us? Since he did not spare his own Son, but gave him up for the sake of all of us, then can we not expect that with him he will freely give us all his gifts?... Can anything cut us off from the love of Christ – can hardships or distress, or persecution, or lack of food and clothing, or threats or violence?... No!

PREPARING FOR RECONCILIATION

SESSION 5

Have you ever seen a movie or a TV show which has a Catholic confession in it? Chances are that you have and that it wasn't anything like what the sacrament of reconciliation is like nowadays. The point of going to confession is that it gives us a way to get our relationship with God back on track. We are forgiven all the things we have done which have got in the way of us living our lives the way God wants and we are able to make a fresh start. It is something to celebrate!

SEE

You won't need to discuss these answers in a group

When did you last have to admit to someone that you had done something wrong?

QUOTE

"Be compassionate just as your Father is compassionate. Do not judge, and you will not be judged; do not condemn, and you will not be condemned; forgive, and you will be forgiven." *From the Gospel of St Luke*

How did it make you feel?

What do you remember about the last time you went to confession to a priest?

How did it make you feel?

Don't worry about how long ago your last confession was.

Share your thoughts on how you feel about going to confession with your group. There is room for your notes here

What happens when people choose not to forgive people?

What happens when people do choose to forgive people?

"Without forgiveness there can be no future for a relationship between individuals or within and between nations." *Archbishop Emeritus Desmond Tutu of Cape Town*

JUDGE

A: Gospel enquiry

This is just one of the many miracles which Jesus performed. This story comes from St Luke's Gospel and it shows us how important the forgiveness of sins is in order to fully become the people we can be. **Luke 5:17-25**

"Now it happened that he was teaching one day… and now some men appeared bringing on a bed a paralysed man whom they were trying to bring in and lay down in front of him. But as they could find no way of getting the man through the crowd, they went up onto the top of the house and lowered him and his stretcher down through the tiles into the middle of the gathering, in front of Jesus. Seeing their faith he said, 'My friend, your sins are forgiven you.' The scribes and the Pharisees began to think this over. 'Who is this man, talking blasphemy? Who but God alone can forgive sins?' But Jesus, aware of their thoughts, made them this reply, 'What are these thoughts you have in your hearts? Which of these is easier: to say "Your sins are forgiven you," or to say "Get up and walk"? But to prove to you that the Son of man has authority on earth to forgive sins,' – he said to the paralysed man – 'I order you: get up and pick up your stretcher and go home.' And immediately before their very eyes he got up, picked up what he had been lying on and went home praising God."

DiSCUSS

- Who is in this story?
- What happened?
- What was said?
- How do you think the man on the stretcher would have reacted to this? Why?
- How do you think the Pharisees and scribes would have reacted to this? Why?
- What does this story say about the forgiveness of sins?

B: What does our faith say?

Today we have the chance to plan our celebration of the sacrament of reconciliation. We want to emphasise CELEBRATE! This is not a chore. It is not something to be nervous of. It is a wonderful gift that the Church gives us. In the last few weeks we have all shared what is important to us and how we think we should live our lives and how God calls us to live.

However, we know that we all fail sometimes. When we fail we need to find a way to make peace, to reconcile ourselves, with God. Think about when you have an argument with your parents. You don't stop loving them and they don't stop loving you. But you can't ignore a big upset. Even though you don't stop loving each other, you still have to make up. It might just be a smile. It might be saying sorry. It may be a hug or a handshake. We need to find a way to express our sorrow and forgiveness and to show that everything is ok.

It is exactly the same with God. Just as we find a way to communicate forgiveness, he finds a way too: in the sacrament of reconciliation. Sometimes you need to give someone a hug to express forgiveness, and that is what God does for us in this sacrament. It's God's language. As we hear God communicating to us, through the words of the priest, it is a chance for us not only to say sorry but for us to really KNOW that God has forgiven us. It doesn't mean he ever stopped loving us. But sometimes we need to know it, and the sacrament of reconciliation gives us that opportunity: it is like a hug from God – a concrete sign of God's love and forgiveness for us.

Discuss what you think about this in your group. What other images from your life could you suggest reconciliation is like? There is room for your notes here:

QUOTE "To those who have been far away from the sacrament of reconciliation and forgiving love, I make this appeal: Come back to this source of grace; do not be afraid! Christ himself is waiting for you. He will heal you, and you will be at peace with God!" *Pope John Paul II*

C: A sacramental sign – the priest

The sacrament of reconciliation is also our chance to say sorry to the whole community. We are all members of a community – of the parish, the school, the nation, the whole Church. Whenever I do something wrong I hurt the community but I can't say sorry to them all. But I can say sorry to the priest who acts on behalf of the whole community. I am not just saying sorry to God, but I am also saying sorry to everyone else and hearing that I am forgiven too.

If your priest is coming to speak to the group, you might want to think of some questions to ask him. There is room to write them down here:

 **"Before you speak, it is necessary for you to listen, for God speaks in the silence of the heart."** *St Teresa*

Going to Confession – Q&A

What do I say to the priest when I go for confession?
Whenever you go up to a priest for individual confession, it is helpful if you mention why you have come to confession and how long it is since you last came to confession. The traditional words most people use are:

"Bless me, Father, for I have sinned. It is

_____ since my last confession."

The priest may then prompt you to tell him your sins or he may be silent, listening, waiting for you to talk about your sins.

There is a prayer, called the Act of Contrition, which you might also use. This will be part of your service of reconciliation:

I confess to almighty God,
and to you,
my brothers and sisters,
that I have sinned through my own fault,
in my thoughts and in my words,
in what I have done,
and in what I have failed to do;
and I ask blessed Mary,
ever virgin,
all the angels and saints,
and you,
my brothers and sisters,
to pray for me to the Lord our God.

Going to Confession – Q&A

What if I have done something and I'm not sure whether it is a sin or not: should I still mention it?
Yes, mention anything you feel you want to get off your conscience. The priest can guide you as to whether it is a sin or not. Even if it isn't something sinful, if something is bothering you, talking it through with a helpful priest can make you feel better.

What if I have forgotten something I did wrong – does that mean it can't be forgiven?
When you go to confession you aren't expected to list absolutely every detail of everything you've done wrong. You are only human. If you genuinely forget something, don't worry, God knows about it and when you receive absolution, all your sins are wiped clean, including the ones you have forgotten about.

Will everyone be able to hear the sins I confess?
No. You will go to confession individually with a priest and only he will hear what you have to say. What you say will be confidential and the priest will never tell anyone else what you have said.

What's absolution?

After you have made your confession of sins, the priest will bless you and say a prayer. Your sins will be forgiven. The Church's special word for this forgiveness that happens in the sacrament of reconciliation is absolution.

What's an act of penance?

At the end of your confession, the priest may ask you to say some prayers or do something as an act of penance. This is part of showing that you are sorry for your sins and that you are willing to take responsibility for them and will do something positive to begin your reconciliation with God.

How often should I go to confession?

There is no correct answer to this. It depends on how much you sin! The Church asks us to go at least once a year. More than that, only you can decide on how often you will go. Most parishes offer confessions once a week, and very often parishes organise special services in the run up to Easter or Christmas. A few keen people go every week, more usually people go before Easter and before Christmas or when a sin is playing on their conscience. Some people don't go for years. This sacrament exists to keep you in a good relationship with God, so only you can know when you need it. Many priests would advise you to try and go once a month so that the sacrament becomes a normal part of your life.

Deciding on your action

So far today we have thought about what the sacrament of reconciliation means and what role it can play in your life. You have also planned out your own service of reconciliation. When we look at how our real lives and faith combine, it leads to action. Once we have thought through God's perspective on our lives we are ready to decide on an action. What are you going to do this week?

Think about how reconciliation helps you to get your relationship with God and with every person back on track. Does it inspire you to choose to do something different this week?

This week I am going to:

If you prefer, you can write this bit in when you get home, or keep it as a secret between you and God.

"There is more joy in heaven over a converted sinner than over a righteous person standing firm…. A farmer has greater love for land which bears fruitfully, after he has cleared it of thorns, than for land which never had thorns but which never yielded a fruitful harvest." *St Gregory the Great*

PRAYER

You don't need to be in church to pray. You can pray anywhere, anytime. Here are some prayers and Bible readings which can help you:

A prayer by St Francis of Assisi, written in the 13th century

Lord, make me an instrument of your peace.
Where there is hatred, let me sow love;
where there is injury, pardon;
where there is doubt, faith;
where there is despair, hope;
where there is darkness, light;
and where there is sadness, joy.

O Divine Master, grant that I may not so much seek
to be consoled as to console;
to be understood as to understand;
to be loved as to love.
For it is in giving that we receive;
it is in pardoning that we are pardoned;
and it is in dying that we are born to eternal life.
Amen.

A prayer

Dear Lord,
today we have been preparing to meet you in the sacrament of reconciliation. May we spend this time of prayer remembering our failings but also being confident that we will soon be fully reconciled to you through your gift of confession.
Amen.

Simple prayer

Dear Jesus,
Sometimes I am confused about what to do. I can't tell which the right decision is. Help me to make good choices.
Amen.

A prayer
Loving Father,
You lift us up from our failings and show us perfection.
You do not offer us what we deserve.
Instead you offer us amazing gifts.
You have given us your Son, and eternal life.
May we return to you through our service of reconciliation
with hearts full of thankfulness and hope.
Amen.

A simple prayer
Lord God,
I know that with your help I will grow into a better person.
I know that you will guide my choices.
Help me to listen to you.
Amen.

Why not try writing a prayer of your own in the space below? Use the prayer to talk to God about the times you have not followed the right path in your life. Ask for forgiveness.

More Bible readings about God's help...

Psalm 130
Out of the depths I cry to you, O Lord,
Lord, hear my voice!
O let your ears be attentive
to the voice of my pleading.

If you, O Lord, should mark our guilt,
Lord, who would survive?
But with you is found forgiveness:
for this we revere you.

Because with the Lord there is mercy
and fullness of redemption,
Israel indeed he will redeem from all its iniquity.

From St Matthew's Gospel
Matthew 18:21
Then Peter went up to him and said, "Lord, how often must I forgive my brother if he wrongs me? As often as seven times?" Jesus answered, "Not seven, I tell you, but seventy-seven times."

From St Paul's letter to the Colossians
Colossians 1:9-14
That is why, ever since the day he told us, we have never failed to remember you in our prayers and ask that through perfect wisdom and spiritual understanding you should reach the fullest knowledge of his will and so be able to lead a life worthy of the Lord, a life acceptable to him in all its aspects, bearing fruit in every kind of good work and growing in knowledge of God, fortified, in accordance with his glorious strength, with all power always to persevere and endure, giving thanks with joy to the Father who has made you able to share the lot of God's holy people and with them to inherit the light. Because that is what he has done. It is he who has rescued us from the ruling force of darkness and transferred us to the kingdom of the Son that he loves, and in him we enjoy our freedom, the forgiveness of sin.

TIME OUT - PRAYER AND THE MASS

SESSION 6

However often you attend Mass, it is easy for it to become so familiar you hardly notice what is going on. Mass isn't just a solemn duty for us. We are all given a challenge to use Mass as a time for celebration and for prayer. It is time out from everyday life. It's a chance for us to take stock, to reflect and to be inspired.

WE BEGIN WITH A PRAYER

Lord Jesus,
We are gathered together here again to prepare
for the sacrament of confirmation. We ask that
you will guide us and inspire us as we have fun,
listen, learn and take part in this session today.
Thank you for your presence here with us today
and always.

Amen.

"Take it and eat… this is my body."
From the Gospel of St Matthew

What do you remember about your First Holy Communion?

Write your ideas here if it helps you

Looking back, do you think that these were the most important things that happened on this day? If not, what do you think was the most important thing about the day?

How do you take time out from the busy-ness of school and daily life?

Have you ever experienced or thought of prayer and going to Church as taking time out?

What do you think might stop some young people from thinking of this as valuable time out?

What wonderful majesty! What stupendous condescension! O sublime humility! That the Lord of the whole universe, God and the Son of God, should humble Himself like this under the form of a little bread, for our salvation."

St Francis of Assisi

JUDGE

A: Gospel enquiry

This is one of the many miracles which Jesus performed. This one is special because it shows how Jesus is generous to us all, and how he gives us all time to be with him. This reading comes from the ninth chapter of **St Luke's Gospel**.

"Jesus made the crowds welcome and talked to them about the kingdom of God; and he cured those who were in need of healing.

It was late afternoon when the Twelve came up to him and said, 'Send the people away and they can go to the villages and farms round about to find lodging and food; for we are in a lonely place here.' He replied, 'Give them something to eat yourselves.' But they said, 'We have no more than five loaves and two fish, unless we are to go ourselves and buy food for all these people.' For there were about five thousand men. But he said to his disciples, 'Get them to sit down in parties of about fifty.' They did so and made them all sit down. Then he took the five loaves and the two fish, raised his eyes to heaven, and said the blessing over them; then he broke them and handed them to his disciples to distribute among the crowd. They all ate as much as they wanted, and when the scraps left over were collected they filled twelve baskets."

- Who is in this story?
- What happened?
- What was said?
- How do you think the disciples would have reacted to this? Why?
- How do you think the people who had come to listen to Jesus would have reacted to this? Why?
- Does this story tell us anything about going to Mass?

B: What does our faith say?

The Church tells us to go to Mass every Sunday. Why? Well, like parents wanting the best for their children, the Church wants the best for us. Mass is good for us, and the Church encourages us to go because it knows this. It is a chance to take time out, to get refreshed and to receive strength and support for the real day-to-day situations of our lives.

Going to Mass is like going away from our homes, studies and everyday life, just like the people in the Gospel who went away to listen to Jesus. In fact, going to Mass can be like going away on a holiday – a 45-minute holiday! When we go on holiday we tend to say that we're leaving everything at home and not taking our worries with us – the course work and revision can wait until I get back! We pack a case and head off to relax for a week or two. Well, that's not entirely true. Usually, almost without knowing it, we take the time away to sort a few things out, to work out some of the big issues in life. Yes, we stop worrying about the small insignificant stuff but sometimes, with the larger situations in life, we find that we come back from time away with a new perspective on them and with new enthusiasm to deal with them. It's the same with going to Mass. Each week we take time away from our everyday life, but bring all the joys and concerns of life with us. We offer all of these things to God in the Mass, so that God can begin to sort them out. Jesus feeds us with his words, and with his presence in Holy Communion, so that we can go back to the world refreshed and with new energy to live life as God wants.

Do you agree that going to Mass should be like this?

Can we consider that taking time to pray might be like this too?

C: A sacramental sign

At each Mass we offer bread and wine, usually with an offertory procession. Two members of the congregation, on our behalf, take the simple elements of bread and wine and give them to the priest, who for us at that moment stands in the place of Christ. What's happening there? We are offering all the real stuff of our lives, the work of our hands and the fruit of the earth. Through that bread and wine we offer all we've achieved, all our joys alongside all our concerns and worries. The priest, representing Christ, then takes our real lives and offers them to the Father in heaven. Then something amazing happens to the bread and wine, for the Church tells us that when we receive Holy Communion we are receiving the real presence of Jesus. It's no longer bread and wine, but the life-giving presence of God. Everything we have offered in the bread and the wine has been made perfect – more than perfect – and been transformed for us into the best gift we have in the entire universe. All of our joys, all of our worries and all of our sorrows are made into something amazing. And we are offered this amazing gift beyond all our imaginings to feed us and nourish us for the return to our daily lives, so that we can transform our lives and the world around us.

The offertory is a time of special prayer, a "holy exchange" with God. In presenting the bread and wine, and other appropriate gifts, we also offer God our lives: all we've achieved, all our joys alongside all our concerns and worries. What would you offer this week?

 **QUOTE** "Then he took a cup, and when he had given thanks he handed it to them, and all drank from it, and he said to them, 'This is my blood, the blood of the covenant, poured out for many.'" *From the Gospel of St Mark*

Meet... Conor

I'm from the north-east of England, and I'm a Catholic because I believe the earth has more relevance than just us being here. I think there's something bigger out there. I go to church even though lots of people tell me it's a waste of time. I do that because I believe in God, and it's a tiny thing that God asks us, to go to church for one hour every week, after all he does for us, just so we can celebrate him, talk about him and be educated about him. If people just called me all the time asking for things, but never did anything in return, that would agitate me.

Going to church furthers my knowledge about Christianity and about Jesus and how he lived his life. It educates me about what I believe in, rather than just "being Catholic" and not knowing anything about it. Sometimes, of course, I don't feel like going to Mass, but even if I go and just sit there I know that God is still present with me.

Jimmy Mizen's family

The day after his sixteenth birthday, Jimmy Mizen and his brother popped into a bakery on their way to buy Jimmy's first ever lottery ticket. In the bakery they were taunted by a nineteen-year-old who then attacked and murdered Jimmy with a broken glass serving dish after he refused to go outside to have a fight.

Jimmy's whole family grieved the loss of this gentle, peaceful young man. His six brothers and two sisters, together with his parents, Barry and Margaret Mizen, decided that some good needed to come out of Jimmy's death. At his funeral his dad said: "Perhaps we all need to look to ourselves and look to the values we would like and our responses to situations in our life. Sometimes we might be drawn into certain ways of living. It is our choice but change has got to come from all of us."

Jimmy's mother wrote about how the family's Catholic faith helped her, in an open letter she wrote to Jimmy after his death: "My faith keeps me going. You know how much I like going to church and I couldn't miss Mass, it gets me through the week. I miss seeing you at the back, at 6ft 4in head and shoulders above everyone else. When tears come at night me and dad say a prayer together. Lighting candles in church also helps me feel better." The family decided not to let hatred take over their lives. Now a foundation in Jimmy's name runs a coffee shop and organises local apprenticeships, it funds minibuses for community projects and perhaps most importantly it campaigns against violence, promoting a legacy of peace.

"Sometimes when I think about what's happened to Jimmy I just want to crawl into a hole, but I pray, I pray to the Holy Spirit, and I am comforted and uplifted and somehow receive the strength to cope."

Margaret Mizen

Deciding on your action

So far we have looked at how going to Mass and receiving communion allow us to share Christ in a special way. We have also thought about how prayer and the Mass give us an opportunity to take time out with God as well as some of the challenges to it.

When we look at how our real lives and faith combine, it leads to action. Once we have thought through God's perspective on our lives we are ready to decide on an action.

"If angels could be jealous of men, they would be so for one reason: Holy Communion."

St Maximilian Kolbe

This week I am going to:

If you prefer, you can write this bit in when you get home, or keep it as a secret between you and God.

What can you pray about?

PRAYER

You don't need to be in church to pray. You can pray anywhere, anytime. Here are some prayers and Bible readings which can help you:

A prayer

Lord Jesus Christ,
In our lives you have given us everything we need and very much more. You came to earth and died on a cross, in forgiveness of sins. You rose again, showing us the way to eternal salvation. And we can experience your presence within us through the gift of Holy Communion which you have given us. Thank you for giving us the gift of yourself in Holy Communion and for giving me the chance to share in it.
Amen.

A prayer

Thank you, Lord Jesus, for guiding me in my life so far. Please be a companion to me throughout my life. Help me to remember that whatever the future holds for me, you will always be present. With you I know that nothing will happen which I cannot cope with when I have the gifts of your help and strength. Amen.

An excerpt from the first letter St Paul wrote to the Christian Community in the city of Corinth (1 Corinthians 10:16-17)
"The blessing cup which we bless, is it not a sharing in the blood of Christ; and the loaf of bread which we break, is it not a sharing in the body of Christ? And as there is one loaf, so we, although there are many of us, are one single body, for we all share in the one loaf."

Simple prayers

Dear Jesus,
Sometimes I don't want to go to Mass, because
I forget what an amazing gift it is that you have
given me. Inspire me when I do go to Mass, so
that through your presence in the Eucharist I
will know your love.
Amen

Lord God,
When I am confused, angry or hurt, hear me
and comfort me.
Through the love of your Son, Jesus Christ.
Amen.

Why not try writing a prayer of your own in
the space below? Use the prayer to talk to God
about things that are on your mind. Perhaps
you could talk to God about something you
need help with.

More Bible readings about finding God's gifts

Luke 22:19-20

Then he took the bread, and when he had given thanks, he broke it and gave it to them, saying, "this is my body given for you; do this in remembrance of me." He did the same with the cup after supper, and said, "This cup is the new covenant in my blood poured out for you."

Psalm 107

O give thanks to the Lord for he is good;
for his great love is without end.

Let them thank the Lord for his love,
for the wonders he does for men.
For he satisfies the thirsty soul;
he fills the hungry with good things.

John 6:35.51-56

"I am the bread of life.
No one who comes to me will ever hunger;
no one who believes in me will ever thirst.
I am the living bread which has come down from heaven.
Anyone who eats this bread will live for ever;
and the bread that I shall give
is my flesh, for the life of the world."
Then the Jews started arguing among themselves,
"How can this man give us his flesh to eat?"
Jesus replied to them:
"In all truth I tell you,
if you do not eat the flesh of the Son of man
and drink his blood,
you have no life in you.
Anyone who does eat my flesh and drink my blood
has eternal life,
and I shall raise that person up on the last day.
For my flesh is real food
and my blood is real drink.
Whoever eats my flesh and drinks my blood lives in me
And I live in that person."

FAITH... IN WHAt? WHAt DO YOU BELiEVE?

SESSION 7

We all have beliefs. From our religious belief to our beliefs and opinions about what other human beings are like, our lives are constantly influenced by what we believe to be true. In this session you have a chance to examine your beliefs and how they affect your life and the lives of others.

WE BEGIN WITH A PRAYER

Lord Jesus,
As we gather here today we ask that you will bless our time together. As we explore our beliefs and the things we hold as most important in our lives, we ask that you will guide us and give us wisdom and insight so that we can learn how to be fully the people you have created us to be.

Amen.

QUOTE

"Everyone who believes may have eternal life."
From the Gospel of St John

SEE

What do you believe to be the most important thing in life?

Write your ideas here if it helps you

Why?

Write your ideas here if it helps you

What do you believe about God?

Write your ideas here if it helps you

The Creed

The Creed is spoken by everyone each week at Mass. We will all say it together during your Confirmation Mass. The Creed is a summary of what Christians believe. By saying it together Christians declare what they believe in a public way.

I believe in one God,
the Father almighty,
maker of heaven and earth,
of all things visible and invisible.
I believe in one Lord Jesus Christ,
the Only Begotten Son of God,
born of the Father before all ages.
God from God, Light from Light,
true God from true God,
begotten, not made,
  consubstantial with the Father;
through him all things were made.
For us men and for our salvation
he came down from heaven,
and by the Holy Spirit was incarnate
  of the Virgin Mary,
and became man.
For our sake he was crucified under
  Pontius Pilate,
he suffered death and was buried,
and rose again on the third day
in accordance with the Scriptures.

He ascended into heaven
and is seated at the right hand of
the Father.
He will come again in glory
to judge the living and the dead
and his kingdom will have no end.
I believe in the Holy Spirit, the
Lord, the giver of life,
who proceeds from the Father
and the Son,
who with the Father and the Son
is adored and glorified,
who has spoken through the
prophets.
I believe in one, holy, catholic and
apostolic Church.
I confess one Baptism for the
forgiveness of sins
and I look forward to the
resurrection of the dead
and the life of the world to come.
Amen.

"Then they said to him 'What must we do if we are to carry out God's work?' Jesus gave them this answer: 'This is carrying out God's work; you must believe in the one he has sent.'" *From the Gospel of St John*

JUDGE

A: Gospel enquiry

This is a reading from St Matthew's Gospel about who the followers of Jesus thought he was.

Matthew chapter 16, verses 13-17

"When Jesus came to the region of Caesarea Philippi he put this question to his disciples, 'Who do people say the Son of man is?' And they said, 'Some say John the Baptist, some Elijah, and others Jeremiah or one of the prophets.' 'But you,' he said, 'who do you say I am?' Then Simon Peter spoke up and said, 'You are the Christ, the Son of the living God.' Jesus replied, 'Simon, son of Jonah, you are a blessed man! Because it was no human agency that revealed this to you but my Father in heaven. So I now say to you: you are Peter and on this rock I will build my community. And the gates of the underworld can never overpower it.'"

Glossary

"Jeremiah and Elijah"
Jeremiah and Elijah were both great prophets in the Old Testament. Jews believe that one day Elijah will return to earth to help the Jewish people.

DISCUSS

- Who is in this story?
- What happened?
- What was said?
- How do you think the apostles felt about being asked this question?
- Why do you think Jesus chose Peter to lead the Church?
- What does this story say about what we believe about Jesus?

At your confirmation you will be asked to state your beliefs. Even though many people in our world do not recognise who God is, you will say in front of your friends and families, and in front of God, that you believe in God.

What difficulties do you think people face in standing up for what they believe in?

Are you prepared to speak about your faith when you are asked?

B: What does our faith say?

During your confirmation the bishop will ask you to renew your baptismal promises. These promises were made on your behalf by your parents when you were baptised. At your confirmation they are your way of saying, "Yes, I believe."

This is the text of the promises you will make:

Renewal of baptismal promises

Bishop: Do you reject Satan and all his works and all his empty promises?
Candidates: **I do.**

Bishop: Do you believe in God, the Father almighty, creator of heaven and earth?
Candidates: **I do.**

Bishop: Do you believe in Jesus Christ, his only Son, our Lord, who was born of the Virgin Mary, was crucified, died, and was buried, rose from the dead, and is now seated at the right hand of the Father?
Candidates: **I do.**

Bishop: Do you believe in the Holy Spirit, the Lord, the giver of life, who came upon the apostles at Pentecost and today is given to you sacramentally in confirmation?
Candidates: **I do.**

Bishop: Do you believe in the holy catholic Church, the communion of saints, the forgiveness of sins, the resurrection of the body and life everlasting?

Candidates: **I do.**

QUOTE

"I could not say I believe. I know! I have had the experience of being gripped by something that is stronger than myself, something that people call God."

Carl Jung, one of the founders of modern psychology

Space here for notes about what you believe about God.

C: A sacramental sign

1. Can you think of times and situations where many people are united together in common belief?

2. How important is it for us to feel that we share common beliefs with others?

3. How can the believing community of the Church be a sign of Christ to others? Can you, as a group, be a sign of Christ to others?

QUOTE

"It is by believing with the heart that you are justified, and by making the declaration with your lips that you are saved." *From the letter St Paul wrote to the Romans*

ACE

Meet... Nicolette

My faith gives me something to rely on. I like the fact that I can pray to God and communicate with God. I ask for things, I thank him for living every day of my life. I'm able to pray to God whenever I'm in need, for example when I'm in an exam, I pray to God, when some of my family members are in need I pray to God: it brings a connection that I need, something greater. I feel that humans need something greater, for them to experience life, to live a good life. Without something greater there is nothing to aspire to be.

In order to live a good life in my opinion you have to fulfill your potential. Fulfilling your potential is doing your calling, whatever you have to do, whatever job or career, do well in school, and be able to work and help others.

Meet Maximilian Kolbe

St Maximilian Kolbe died as Prisoner 16670 in Auschwitz concentration camp on 14 August 1941.

Fr Maximilian Kolbe was a Franciscan friar and a priest. Long before his extraordinary death he had already achieved great things. He set up a huge religious community in Poland, then went on missions to establish churches in Japan and India. He later returned to Poland and ran the publishing company and radio station dedicated to Mary, the Mother of God, which he had established.

During the 1930s he openly spoke out against the Nazis, and when they invaded Poland, Kolbe was imprisoned twice. The first time he was released after three months, but he didn't stop speaking out. His second imprisonment took him to the concentration camp in Auschwitz. Again he stayed a prisoner for three months, but this time his release came from death.

© Catholic News Service

One day a prisoner escaped from Auschwitz. The camp commander demanded that ten prisoners be put to death to be an example to prevent others from escaping. Ten were chosen at random, but Fr Maximilian stepped forward and offered to take the place of one man who he knew was a husband and father. Francis Gajowniczek was allowed to live and Fr Maximilian was sent to die in his place. Fr Maximilian died of an injection of poison after four days in darkness with no food or water.

When Pope John Paul made him a saint in 1982, there was a special guest in the congregation – Francis Gajowniczek.

QUOTE "Beyond armies of occupation and the hecatombs of extermination camps, there are two irreconcilable enemies in the depth of every soul: good and evil, sin and love. And what use are the victories on the battlefield if we are ourselves defeated in our innermost personal selves?" *St Maximilian Kolbe*

QUOTE "Maximilian did not die but 'gave his life... for his brother.' In that death, terrible from the human point of view, there was the whole definitive greatness of the human act and of the human choice. He spontaneously offered himself up to death out of love." *Pope John Paul II*

Deciding on your action

So far we have looked at what we believe and what that means in our lives. We have also looked at the promises we will make at our confirmation.

When we look at how our real lives and faith combine, it leads to action. Once we have thought through God's perspective on our lives we are ready to decide on an action.

"Faith is to believe what you do not see; the reward of this faith is to see what you believe." *St Augustine*

Think about what you promised to do last week. Did you do it? How did it go? How did you feel? If you want to share your experience with the group you can but you are under no pressure to share this if you don't want to.

Think about what you might do this week. It might be sorting out a disagreement you have had with someone, or dealing with an issue you feel is unresolved. Or it could be you reaching out to someone who needs your help.

This week I am going to:

If you prefer, you can write this bit in when you get home, or keep it as a secret between you and God.

PRAYER

You don't need to be in church to pray. You can pray anywhere, anytime. Here are some prayers and Bible readings which can help you:

A reading
(This comes from the Gospel of St John)
For this is how God loved the world:
He gave his only Son,
So that everyone who believes in him may not perish
But may have eternal life.
For God sent his Son into the world
Not to judge the world,
But so that through him the world might be saved.

A prayer
Our God, who is three in one, Father, Son and Holy Spirit,
Be present here with us as we pray.
Strengthen our belief and our faith.
Inspire us and bring us to the fullness of life which you offer to us all.
Amen.

A prayer
Thank you God for the love you have shown me.
There are going to be times when I doubt you.
When this happens, please help me to come back to you
And to feel the love which you bring into our lives.
Amen.

From Psalm 27

The Lord is my light and my help;
whom shall I fear?
The Lord is the stronghold of my life;
before whom shall I shrink?

Though an army encamp against me
my heart would not fear.
Though war break out against me
even then would I trust.

I am sure I shall see the Lord's goodness
in the land of the living.
Hope in him, hold firm and take heart.
Hope in the Lord!

Why not try writing a prayer of your own in
the space to the right? Use the prayer to talk
to God about your identity – the person you
are and the person you want to become. Talk
to God about being a member of God's family
and what that means to you.

A simple prayer

Lord God, I do believe in you, but it is hard to
follow you.
You want me to always do the right thing but
sometimes there's a lot of pressure on me to do
things that I'm not sure are right. Strengthen
me to choose your ways, not the world's ways.
Amen.

More Bible readings about God's help...

Matthew 9:27-30

As Jesus went on his way two blind men followed him shouting, "Take pity on us, son of David." And when Jesus reached the house the blind men came up to him and he said to them, "Do you believe I can do this?" They said, "Lord, we do." Then he touched their eyes saying, "According to your faith, let it be done to you." And their sight returned.

James 2:14-17

How does it help… when someone who has never done a single good act claims to have faith? Will that faith bring salvation? If one of the brothers or one of the sisters is in need of clothes and has not enough food to live on and one of you says to them, "I wish you well; keep yourself warm and eat plenty," without giving them these bare necessities of life, then what good is that? In the same way faith, if good deeds do not go with it, is quite dead.

Mark 11:23-25

Have faith in God. I tell you solemnly, if anyone says to this mountain, "Be pulled up and thrown into the sea," with no doubt in his heart, but believing that what he says will happen, it will be done for him. I tell you, therefore, everything you ask and pray for, believe that you have it already, and it will be yours. And when you stand in prayer, forgive whatever you have against anybody, so that your Father in heaven may forgive your failings too.

Isaiah 43:10-13

You yourselves are my witnesses, declares the Lord, and the servant whom I have chosen, so that you may know and believe me and understand that it is I. No god was formed before me, nor will be after me. I, I am the Lord, and there is no other Saviour but me. I have revealed, have saved and have proclaimed … I am God, yes from eternity I am.

Mark 1:40-42

A leper came to him and pleaded on his knees: "If you want to," he said, "you can cure me." Feeling sorry for him, Jesus stretched out his hand and touched him. "Of course I want to!" he said. "Be cured!" And the leprosy left him at once and he was cured.

Ephesians 1:3-8

Blessed be God the Father of our Lord Jesus Christ,
Who has blessed us with all the spiritual blessings of heaven in Christ.
Before the world was made, he chose us, chose us in Christ,
To be holy and spotless, and to live through love in his presence,
Determining that we should become his adopted sons, through Jesus
  Christ for his own kind purposes,
To make us praise the glory of his grace,
His free gift to us in the Beloved,
In whom, through his blood, we gain our freedom, the forgiveness of
  our sins.
Such is the richness of the grace which he has showered on us in all
wisdom and insight.

Philippians 1:3-5. 9-10

I thank my God whenever I think of you; and every time I pray for all of you, I pray with joy, remembering how you have helped to spread the Good News from the day you first heard it right up to the present. My prayer is that your love for each other may increase more and more and never stop improving your knowledge and deepening your perception so that you can always recognise what is best. This will help you become pure and blameless, and prepare you for the Day of Christ.

PREPARING THE CONFIRMATION MASS

SESSION 8

The day of your confirmation is fast approaching. Your preparation is almost complete. You are nearly ready to receive the gifts of the Holy Spirit and to embark on your new life as a confirmed Christian. Hopefully your Catholic faith has grown over the past few weeks as you have shared, learned and used what you have learned in your life. Today you will prepare the Confirmation Mass so that the sacrament really will feel like your special occasion.

SEE

Write down some words that describe how you are feeling about your confirmation.

QUOTE

"Send out your Spirit and life begins; you renew the face of the earth." *From Psalm 104*

How are you feeling about your confirmation?

SEE

Do you think it is important to commit yourself to being a Christian? Why?

What have you chosen as your confirmation name?

Why did you choose this name?

Do you know anything about the saint who had this name?

 "You must be as lighted lanterns and shine like brilliant chandeliers among men. By your good example and your words, animate others to know and love God." *St Mary Joseph Rossello*

Who have you chosen as your sponsor?

Why have you chosen her/him?

JUDGE

A: Choosing the readings for the Confirmation Mass

Read the readings your catechist has provided and discuss the following questions with your group. You can use this page to make notes if you want to.

What happened in the reading?

What does this say about being confirmed?

Do you like this reading?

Which reading do you want to be in your Confirmation Mass?

Which reading has your small group agreed to recommend to the whole group?

Why do you think this reading is appropriate for your Confirmation Mass?

Getting yourself ready for your confirmation

It's all very well choosing readings or going into the church to practise where you are going to stand during the Mass. It all helps you to prepare. But the most important preparation for your confirmation goes on inside your own heart and your own mind. Over the last few weeks you have met in a group to get ready to receive the sacrament. Working as a group has been important.

Now it is the time to do some work by yourself. Or rather, not by yourself, with God. In the days leading up to your confirmation day, try to set aside a little time – just a few minutes – to pray and to listen to God. You could use some of the prayers at the end of this chapter, or from any of the other sessions.

"There is a variety of gifts but always the same Spirit; there are all sorts of service to be done, but always to the same Lord; working in all sorts of different ways in different people."

St Paul's first letter to the Corinthians

Deciding on your action

So far today we have prepared the liturgy for your Confirmation Mass. We have also thought about how we feel about becoming confirmed. When we look at how our real lives and faith combine, it leads to action. Once we have thought through God's perspective on our lives we are ready to decide on an action.

"Those whose hearts are pure are temples of the Holy Spirit."
St Lucy

Personal action

Think about what your life will be like after your confirmation. What commitment or commitments will you make to your new life as a confirmed Christian?

"Trying to do the Lord's work in your own strength is the most confusing, exhausting, and tedious of all work. But when you are filled with the Holy Spirit, then the ministry of Jesus just flows out of you." *Corrie ten Boom*

Group action – preparing the bidding prayers

Use this space to draft some ideas for a bidding prayer to be said in your Confirmation Mass

Here's one prayer format which might help you:
Lord, we pray for

_____ (subject):
that

_____ (intention).
Lord, in your mercy: hear our prayer.

e.g. Lord, we pray for everyone being confirmed this year: that their hearts may be filled with love for you and for one another. Lord, in your mercy: hear our prayer.

PRAYER

You don't need to be in church to pray. You can pray anywhere, anytime. Here are some prayers and Bible readings which can help you:

This prayer is attributed to St Patrick

Christ with me, Christ before me, Christ behind me,
Christ in me, Christ beneath me, Christ above me,
Christ on my right, Christ on my left,
Christ when I lie down, Christ when I sit down,
Christ when I arise,
Christ in the heart of every person who thinks of me,
Christ in the mouth of everyone who speaks of me,
Christ in every eye that sees me,
Christ in every ear that hears me.

A prayer

Lord Jesus,
When you returned to heaven from earth, you promised to send your Holy Spirit to dwell within your followers. Make us worthy in our hearts, so that we will be ready to receive the gifts of the Spirit when we receive the sacrament of confirmation.
Amen.

A prayer

Loving Father,
In the days before my confirmation, may I concentrate on the sacrament I will receive so that the celebration may be full of joy; and may I not be too distracted by all the new clothes and parties which surround it. Thank you for the time we have had in this group preparing for our confirmation. May we always draw strength and comfort from what we have learned together.
Amen.

From Psalm 42

Like the deer that yearns
for running streams,
so my soul is yearning
for you, my God.

My soul is thirsting for God,
the God of my life;
when can I enter and see
the face of God?

Why are you cast down, my soul,
why groan within me?
Hope in God; I will praise him still,
my saviour and my God.

Why not try writing a prayer of your own in the space to the right? Use the prayer to talk to God about what you hope for in your life and what you are worried about. Perhaps you could talk to God about how you are feeling about your confirmation and your new life as a confirmed Christian.

A simple prayer

Dear Jesus,
I am worried about my confirmation. I am worried that receiving the Holy Spirit will make me have to change my life and I am worried about what that will involve. Help me to listen to you and to trust you.
Amen.

More Bible readings about the Holy Spirit...

Isaiah 61:1-2
The spirit of the Lord is upon me, for the Lord has anointed me. He has sent me to bring the news to the afflicted, to soothe the broken-hearted, to proclaim liberty to captives, release to those in prison, to comfort all who mourn.

Matthew 28: 18-20
Jesus came up and spoke to them. He said, "All authority in heaven and on earth has been given to me. Go, therefore, make disciples of all nations; baptise them in the name of the Father and of the Son and of the Holy Spirit, and teach them to observe all the commands I gave you. And look, I am with you always; yes, to the end of time."

Ephesians 3:14-19
This, then, is what I pray, kneeling before the Father. In the abundance of his glory may he, through his Spirit, enable you to grow firm in power with regard to your inner self, so that Christ may live in your hearts through faith, and then, planted in love and built on love, with all God's holy people you will have the strength to grasp the breadth and the length, the height and the depth; so that, knowing the love of Christ, which is beyond knowledge, you may be filled with the utter fullness of God.

Actively Living Life

Session 9

Now you are a confirmed Christian. Congratulations! In this session you have a chance to follow up what you have learned about your faith and think about how it can help you as you go about your life in the future.

WE BEGIN WITH A PRAYER

Lord Jesus,
Thank you for the gifts of your Holy Spirit which we received at our confirmation. Thank you for the love of our family and friends and all those who came to support us on our confirmation day. Now that we have been confirmed, strengthen us as we move forward into our new lives as confirmed Christians.

Amen.

QUOTE

"You will go out with joy and be led away in safety.
Mountains and hills will break into joyful cries before you and all the trees of the countryside clap their hands."

From the book of Isaiah

What has happened this week that has made you think or caused you concern?

Write your ideas here if it helps you

What do you think a leader is? How do you spot a leader? What qualities does he or she have? Do you know any good leaders? What do they do? What is special about them?

Write your ideas here if it helps you

Who and what do you think people your age are prepared to be led by?

JUDGE

A: "Anyone who wants to be first among you must be slave to all"

This is a reading from St Mark's Gospel about how to follow Jesus. **Mark chapter 10, verses 41-45**

"When the other ten heard this they began to feel indignant with James and John, so Jesus called them to him and said to them, 'You know that among the gentiles those they call their rulers lord it over them, and their great men make their authority felt. Among you this is not to happen. No; anyone who wants to become great among you must be your servant, and anyone who wants to be first among you must be slave to all. For the Son of man himself came not to be served but to serve, and to give his life as a ransom for many.'"

Glossary

"Gentile"
The word was used by Jews to describe someone who was not Jewish. So we are all gentiles as well as being Christians.

DISCUSS

- Who is in this story?
- What happened?
- What was said?
- How do you think the apostles present would have reacted to this?
- What kind of life is Jesus calling us to lead in this Gospel story?

Throughout the Gospels Jesus always turns things on their head! *If we want to be great, we must be a servant; if we want to be first, we must be last!*

Jesus is not saying that we cannot do great things, but rather that we must not use our achievements as a way of overshadowing others. Everything that we do should be for the benefit of those around us, and never at anyone else's expense. At your confirmation you said to the whole Church and to God that you want to share in the life of Jesus. And Jesus has shown us, by the way he lived, that the way to share in his life is to love our neighbours.

B: What does our faith say?

As baptised and confirmed Catholic Christians, we are called to **lead** our lives in a certain way; that is to say that we are called always to follow Jesus Christ as The Way. We are also called to be **leaders** in our own lives. But the type of leaders we are meant to be is very different from the type of leaders we often see around us in the world.

What do you think a Christian leader is?

What qualities do they have?

C: Why bother?

Sometimes we look around us at the world and think that our lives cannot make a difference. The world just has too many problems. After all, what we do won't be noticed anyway. But there are loads of examples of people who really have made a difference. And each one of us can make the world a better place to live in even if it is just in small ways.

© Túrelio, 1986

St Teresa only ever did small things. She reached out to the poor she saw around her, by leaving her religious order and using her basic medical training to tend to those in need. Gradually she built up a religious community of fellow nuns to work with the poor in Calcutta (now Kolkata), the Indian city where she lived. As she saw needs, she tried to meet them through medical care, education, orphanages and food distribution. She did not set out to establish a global organization but that is what she did, little by little. Her order, the Missionaries of Charity, now have missions in 120 countries around the world.

QUOTE **"We ourselves feel that what we are doing is just a drop in the ocean. But if that drop was not in the ocean, I think the ocean would be less because of that missing drop. I do not agree with the big way of doing things."** *St Teresa of Calcutta (1910-1997)*

What do you think about the quotation St Teresa of Calcutta gave?

St Teresa was serving the poor in Calcutta because that's where she saw the need. What situations did you share at the beginning of the session? Do you see the need to make a difference?

What situations might you be called to be leaders in?

Deciding on your action

So far we have looked at what makes a good leader, what we are led by and what makes Christian leaders different. We have also thought about things that cause us concern and what we might do to take a lead in those situations.

When we look at how our real lives and faith combine, it leads to action. Once we have thought through God's perspective on our lives we are ready to decide on an action.

"Love God, serve God: everything is in that."
St Clare of Assisi

Personal action

Think about what you promised to do the last time this group met for a preparation session before your confirmation. Did you do it? How did it go? How did you feel? If you want to share your experience with the group you can but you are under no pressure to share this if you don't want to.

Think about what you might do this week, and in the weeks, months and years to come, to live as a Christian leader.

I am going to:

If you prefer, you can write this bit in when you get home, or keep it as a secret between you and God.

Group action

Where do you want to go next as a group?
Do you think you would like to keep meeting up? What could you do? The group leaders might make some suggestions for you to consider; you could also write down your own ideas below to discuss with the group.

PRAYER

You don't need to be in church to pray. You can pray anywhere, anytime. Here are some prayers and Bible readings which can help you:

A prayer
For all the fun we have had.
Thank you, Lord.
For all that we have learned.
Thank you, Lord.
For the times when we have prayed together.
Thank you, Lord.
And for the memories we have gathered.
Thank you, Lord.
Amen.

Simple prayers
Dear God, as I grow and change in the future
Keep me close to you,
Keep me faithful to you,
As I will try to keep close and faithful to you.
Amen.

A prayer
Thank you, Lord,
for this group and all that we have done together.
Now it is time for us to leave
and to find our own ways to follow you for the rest of our lives.
Guide us and strengthen us through gifts of your Holy Spirit.
May we always know your love
and find comfort in our faith and trust in you.
Amen.

Reading

This reading comes from Psalm 100

Cry out with joy to the Lord, all the earth.
Serve the Lord with gladness.
Come before him, singing for joy.

Know that he, the Lord, is God.
He made us, we belong to him,
We are his people, the sheep of his flock.

Go within his gates, giving thanks.
Enter his courts with songs of praise.
Give thanks to him and bless his name.

Indeed, how good is the Lord,
Eternal his merciful love.
He is faithful from age to age.

Why not try writing a prayer of your own in the space below? Use the prayer to talk to God about your identity – the person you are and the person you want to become. Talk to God about being a member of God's family and what that means to you.

More Bible readings about following God throughout life...

Isaiah 43:1-2

Do not be afraid, for I have redeemed you;
I have called you by your name, you are mine.
Should you pass through the waters, I shall be with you;
Or through rivers, they will not swallow you up.
Should you walk through fire, you will not suffer,
And the flame will not burn you.

1 Chronicles 16:8-11

Give thanks to the Lord,
Call his name aloud,
Proclaim his deeds to the peoples.
Chant to him, play to him,
Sing about all his wonders!

Take pride in his holy name,
Let your heart rejoice, you seekers of the Lord!
Seek out the Lord, seek his strength,
Continually seek out his presence!

Matthew 6:25-34

I am telling you not to worry about your life and what you are to eat, nor about your body and what you are to wear. Surely life is more than food, and the body more than clothing! Look at the birds in the sky. They do not sow or reap or gather into barns; yet your heavenly Father feeds them. Are you not worth much more than they are? Can any of you, however much you worry, add one single cubit to your span of life? And why worry about clothing? Think of the flowers growing in the fields; they never have to work or spin; yet I assure you that not even Solomon in all his royal robes was clothed like one of these. Now if that is how God clothes the wild flowers… will he not much more look after you, you who have so little faith?… So do not worry about tomorrow: tomorrow will take care of itself. Each day has enough trouble of its own.

Mark 8:34-35

He called the people and his disciples to him and said, "If anyone wants to be a follower of mine, let him renounce himself and take up his cross and follow me. Anyone who wants to save his life will lose it; but anyone who loses his life for my sake, and for the sake of the gospel, will save it.

2 Corinthians 5:20–6:1

So we are ambassadors for Christ; it is as though God were urging you through us, and in the name of Christ we appeal to you to be reconciled to God. For our sake he made the sinless one a victim for sin, so that in him we might become the uprightness of God. As his fellow-workers, we urge you not to let your acceptance of his grace come to nothing.

Truth: My Journal

Published by **Redemptorist Publications**
Alphonsus House, Chawton, Hampshire, GU34 3HQ UK
Tel. +44 (0)1420 88222, Fax +44 (0)1420 88805
Email rp@rpbooks.co.uk, www.rpbooks.co.uk

A registered charity limited by guarantee. Registered in England: 3261721.

First published September 2011.
Revised December 2014.

Layout and cover design by Chris Nutbeen.

Course concept devised and written by Danny Curtin.
Additional material by Marguerite Hutchinson and Andrew Lyon.

Edited by Marguerite Hutchinson.

ISBN 978-085231-389-3

A CIP catalogue record for this book is available from the British Library.

Printed by Bishops Printers, Portsmouth PO6 1TR.